KEYBC...

C000273445

TRINITY
COLLEGE LONDON

THE EXAM
AT A GLANCE

For your Rock & Pop exam you will need to perform a set of **three songs** and one of the **Session skills** assessments, either **Playback** or **Improvising**. You can choose the order in which you play your set-list.

Song 1

Choose a song from this book

OR from www.trinityrock.com/downloads.

Song 2

Choose a different song from this book

OR from www.trinityrock.com/downloads

OR perform a song you have chosen yourself: this could be your own cover version or a song you have written. It should be at the same level as the songs in this book.

Song 3: Technical focus

Choose one of the Technical focus songs from this book, which cover three specific technical elements.

Session skills

Choose either **Playback** or **Improvising**.

When you are preparing for your exam please check on **www.trinityrock.com** for the most up-to-date information and requirements as these can change from time to time.

CONTENTS

Songs	The Climb	4
	Let's Dance	6
	If You Don't Know Me By Now	8
	Freight Train	10
Technical focus songs	Insomnia	13
	I Believe I'll Dust My Broom	16
About the songs	The Climb	20
	Let's Dance	21
	If You Don't Know Me By Now	22
	Freight Train	23
	Insomnia	24
	I Believe I'll Dust My Broom	25
Session skills	Playback	26
	Improvising	28
Help pages	Choosing a song for your exam	29
	Writing your own song	30
	Playing in a band	31
	Playing with backing tracks	32
	Copyright in a song	32

Trinity College London's Rock & Pop syllabus and supporting publications have been devised and produced in association with Faber Music and Peters Edition London.

Trinity College London
Registered office:
89 Albert Embankment
London SE1 7TP UK
T + 44 (0)20 7820 6100
F + 44 (0)20 7820 6161
E music@trinitycollege.co.uk
www.trinitycollege.co.uk

Registered in the UK. Company no. 02683033
Charity no. 1014792
Patron HRH The Duke of Kent KG

Copyright © 2012 Trinity College London
First published in 2012 by Trinity College London

Cover and book design by Chloë Alexander
Brand development by Andy Ashburner @ Caffeinehit (www.caffeinehit.com)
Photographs courtesy of Rex Features Limited
Printed in England by Caligraving Ltd

Audio produced, mixed and mastered by Tom Fleming
Piano and keyboards arranged by Oliver Weeks
Backing tracks arranged by Tom Fleming

Musicians
Vocals: Bo Walton, Brendan Reilly & Alison Symons
Keyboards: Oliver Weeks
Guitar & Bass: Tom Fleming
Bass: Ben Hillyard
Drums: George Double
Studio Engineer: Joel Davies www.thelimehouse.com

All rights reserved

ISBN: 978-0-85736-237-7

SONGS THE CLIMB

TRACK 1 demo TRACK 2 backing

Miley Cyrus
Words and Music by Jessica Alexander and Jon Mabe

♩ = 80 **Pop Ballad** *2 bars count-in*

Lyrics:
I can al-most see____ it, that dream I'm dream-ing, but there's a voice in-side my head saying, you'll ne-ver reach it. Ev'ry step I'm tak-ing, ev'ry move I make feels lost with no di-rec-tion, my faith is shak-ing, but I, got-ta keep

Chris Montez
Words and Music by Jim Lee

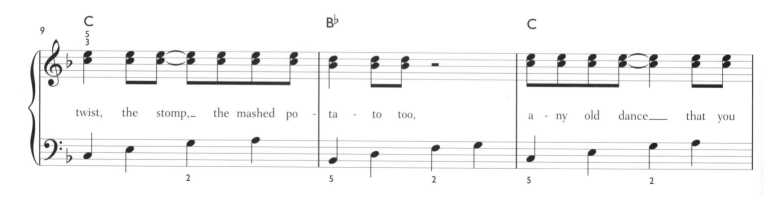

SONGS

IF YOU DON'T KNOW ME BY NOW

Harold Melvin And The Blue Notes
Words and Music by Kenneth Gamble and Leon Huff

you should un - der - stand me, like I

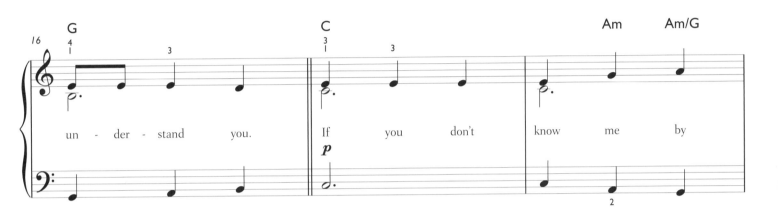

un - der - stand you. If you don't know me by

now_____ you will nev - er, nev - er, nev - er

rit.

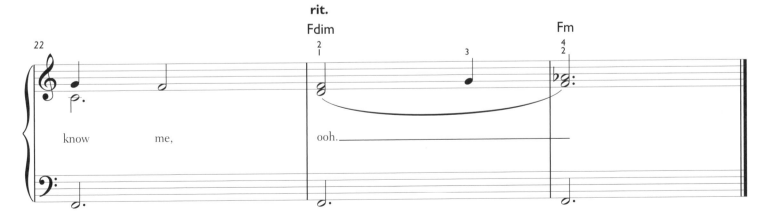

know me, ooh._____

SONGS FREIGHT TRAIN

Taj Mahal
Words and Music by Paul James, Fred Williams and Elizabeth Cotten

1. Freight train, freight train, go - in' so fast,_____

freight train, freight train go - in' so fast._____

www.trinityrock.com

Please don't tell what train I'm on, so they

won't know where I've gone.

2. When I die, please bu-ry me deep,___

down   the   end   of   old Chest - nut Street.___   So

I   can   hear   old   num - ber   nine   as

she   goes   roll - in'   by.

INSOMNIA

In your exam, you will be assessed on the following technical elements:

1 Rhythmic control

A riff is a phrase that is repeated throughout a song. 'Insomnia' has a famous two-bar riff which starts at bar 13: the same rhythm is then repeated for the rest of the song. Try clapping the rhythm very slowly while tapping your foot:

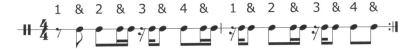

When you are comfortable with this rhythm, try the riff. Don't play it up to speed straight away. Start slower and practise with a metronome, gradually building up the speed until it feels like second nature. This two-bar rhythm is repeated throughout the song, so it is worth practising it.

2 Articulation

Articulation describes how you play the notes. There are three types of articulation in 'Insomnia':

- **Staccato**: indicated by dots above or below the note, (see the opening section in the left hand). *Staccato* notes should be played short and detached. Bounce your fingers off the keys to produce a short note with no sustain.
- **Tenuto**: indicated by short lines above or below the notes (see bar 21). Play these notes broadly – a bit louder and slightly separated – to give them added importance.
- **Accents**: the last note of 'Insomnia' has an accent (>). Play this note louder and very marked. There is also an accent in bar 9.

3 Dynamics

This song has several dynamic markings (which tell you how loudly or quietly to play):

- ***p*** (*piano* = quiet)
- ***mf*** (*mezzo forte* = moderately loud)
- ***f*** (*forte* = loud)
- ***ff*** (*fortissimo* = very loud)

Be prepared for passages where the dynamics suddenly change. For example, the opening should be quiet and *staccato* in the left hand. Then at bar 9 the left hand is moderately loud with an accented note (but the right hand should continue to play quietly). Most of the long riff section is loud – make sure you stay loud, with the very last note louder and accented.

TECHNICAL FOCUS SONGS

INSOMNIA

TRACK 9 demo — TRACK 10 backing

Faithless
Words and Music by Maxi Jazz, Ayalah Bentovim and Rollo Armstrong

♩ = 120 **Menacing** *2 bars count-in*

p Deep in the bo-som of the gen-tle night— is when I search for the light,— pick up my

pen and start to write, I struggle and fight dark for-ces in the clear moon-light— with-out fear,—

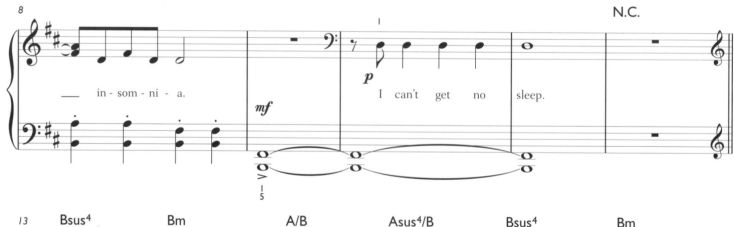

— in-som-ni-a. I can't get no sleep.

I BELIEVE I'LL DUST MY BROOM

In your exam, you will be assessed on the following technical elements:

1 Stop time

Bars 15–18 only have one chord per bar – accented ♪ notes on the first beat of each bar. This is known as a 'stop time' section. Make these chords short and loud and make sure they are exactly in time – it is tempting to rush. Count a steady **1 2 3 4** in your head and listen to the bass drum part which plays the same rhythm – make sure you are together with the drums.

2 Blue notes

An accidental is a sharp (♯), flat (♭) or natural (♮) used during the song but not found in the key signature. 'Dust My Broom' is in the key of A major and so the key signature has three sharps. But this is a blues song and uses several flattened blue notes; for example C♮, G♮ and E♭. An accidental sign lasts for the whole bar – in bar 6, for example, the ♮ applies to the G in both chords.

3 Syncopation

Syncopation is where the rhythm is off the beat. There are two main rhythms in the keyboards part of 'Dust My Broom' – both use syncopation. The first section (bars 3–13) has a steady ♩ beat in the left hand while the right hand plays the syncopation. The second chord is dotted, so lasts to the end of the bar.

The second main section (bars 19–22) again has a steady beat in the left hand while the right hand plays off the beat at the end of each bar. Once again, the last note is dotted, so lasts until the end of the bar.

There are other examples of syncopation throughout the song – watch out for them.

BAND OPTION

TRACK 11 demo TRACK 12 backing

I BELIEVE I'LL DUST MY BROOM

Robert Johnson
Words and Music by Robert Johnson

A major - F♯ C♯ G♯

♩ = 100 **Blues** *2 bars count-in*

he can have my room.___

(Guitar solo)

(Keyboard solo)

(Bass solo)

I be-

THE CLIMB

Miley Cyrus
from 'Hannah Montana: The Movie'

Miley Cyrus is from Nashville, Tennessee. She was the star of *Hannah Montana*, a popular Disney Channel television series, in which she played a teenage girl leading a double life – by day an ordinary 14-year-old school girl, by night a famous pop star. In 2009, the television programme was made into a film, *Hannah Montana: The Movie*. 'The Climb' is the very popular lead song from the soundtrack. It was also the winning *X-factor* song in 2009, sung by Joe McElderry.

'The Climb' starts with a nice steady ♩♩♩♩ beat – this sets the speed for the rest of the song. Be careful not to rush here, otherwise you will have trouble when you have to fit in the ♫♫. The tune has the same rhythm as the words, which will help you to get the timing right.

Play the slurs (⌢) in bars 3, 4, 13, 21 and 23 as smoothly as you can – so the pairs of notes are joined together without a gap in between. The other notes should be more separated.

The first page of this song should be played *p* (*piano* = quiet) and *mp* (*mezzo piano* = moderately quiet), while most of the second page should be *mf* (*mezzo forte* = moderately loud). Make sure you can hear the difference.

'Ain't *about* how *fast* I *get* there'

LET'S DANCE

Chris Montez

The American singer Chris Montez grew up in Los Angeles and had a brief but successful career during the 1960s and early 1970s. He is best known for his 1962 single 'Let's Dance', which was an international chart success.

There are many cover versions of 'Let's Dance': the most well-known is by Slade, with other versions by the punk band Ramones and the rock band Status Quo. It also featured in the 1978 comedy film *National Lampoon's Animal House*.

The tune in the right hand has the same rhythm as the words, which will help you to get the rhythm right.

This song has two different dynamic markings. Look out for:
- ***mf*** (*mezzo forte* = moderately loud)
- ***f*** (*forte* = loud)

Bar 20 has a ⟨crescendo⟩. This is a *crescendo* – it tells you to get gradually louder. Try to make each beat louder than the one before until you reach the next bar. Then you should play loudly (***f***) until the end of the song.

Look out for the accents (>) in the piano solo towards the end of the song. Make sure that the accented notes are louder than the others.

The word 'rall.' in the penultimate bar is short for *rallentando*. This means that you should gradually slow down.

'Hey *baby* won't you *take* a *chance?*'

IF YOU DON'T KNOW ME BY NOW

Harold Melvin And The Blue Notes

The group Harold Melvin And The Blue Notes were formed in 1954 in Philadelphia, USA. They had a varied repertoire that included soul, R&B and doo-wop. Although they had a number of minor hits at the beginning of their career, they only became truly successful when Teddy Pendergrass, the drummer in the band, became the singer.

When the band was signed to the Philadelphia International label, Harold Melvin became a driving force behind Philadelphia soul – notable for its lavish productions that featured strings and soulful vocals. 'If You Don't Know Me By Now' was a massive 'Philly' soul hit for Harold Melvin and, some years later, for Simply Red.

'If You Don't Know Me By Now' has a lovely lyrical melody in the right hand – make sure that you can hear the top line above the other notes. The song is in $\frac{3}{4}$ so should have a flowing feel like a waltz.

The tune in the right hand has the same rhythm as the words, which will help you to get the rhythm right.

In the first eight bars, make sure that you hold the ♩. under the tune for the full three beats.

The instruction at the top of the page says 'Slightly swung'. This means that when you come to the ♫ you should make the first of each pair slightly longer.

'All the things that we've been through'

www.trinityrock.com

FREIGHT TRAIN

Taj Mahal

'Freight Train' was written in the early 20th century by Elizabeth Cotten, when she was only 12 years old. She was self-taught and played the guitar left-handed (but without restringing it), so used her thumb to play the melody and fingers to play bass and harmony. She did not start recording and performing in public until she was in her sixties, but still went on to win major awards.

'Freight Train' became very popular during the American folk revival in the 1950s and 1960s, when many artists covered it, including Peter, Paul and Mary, and Joan Baez. It is now considered to be an American folk classic. This version is based on the cover by the American blues musician Taj Mahal.

PERFORMANCE · HINTS & TIPS ·

The rhythm in bar 1 of 'Freight Train' repeats for most of the song. Make sure that you can play this rhythm securely.

- It should sound a bit like a guitar being fingerpicked.
- Think of the left hand as being the 'straight' part – steady ♩ ♩ – which the right hand bounces off.
- Listen to the steady ♩♩♩♩ drum beat in the verses – it helps you keep in time.

'Freight Train' should be played moderately loudly (***mf***) nearly all the way through.

This song is also in the vocals, guitar, bass and drums books so you can get together and play it in a band.

'Please *don't tell* what *train* I'm on'

INSOMNIA

Faithless

'Insomnia' was the second single recorded by the UK dance group Faithless – a British electronica band made up of Rollo (the brother of singer Dido), Maxi Jazz and Sister Bliss.

Taken from the group's first album, *Reverence* (1996), 'Insomnia' is classic acid house (a type of dance music using a four-on-the-floor beat, samples and synthesisers). Featuring Maxi Jazz singing as an insomniac while he struggles to sleep, the song was popular with dance music fans during the 24-hour rave scene of the 1990s. There have been many remixes of the song.

PERFORMANCE · HINTS & TIPS ·

You should play the first section in a hushed manner: try to make it sound menacing. The left-hand ***mf*** (*mezzo forte* = moderately loud) chord at bar 9 should be a bit louder, but not too loud.

Bar 12 is silent. Count **1 2 3 4** in your head so that you come back in correctly on the first beat of the next bar.

Watch out for the change to the treble clef in the left hand in bar 13, and back to the bass clef in bar 21.

The abbreviation '*sim.*' at bar 15 means 'continue in a similar way'. Here it is telling you to continue playing the right-hand notes *staccato* (which means short and detached).

'*I struggle* and fight *dark* forces'

I BELIEVE I'LL DUST MY BROOM

Robert Johnson

'Dust My Broom' is a 12-bar blues song first recorded by the Mississippi blues singer and guitarist Robert Johnson (1911–1938). Like most blues (early American black music originally performed by one singer accompanied on guitar or banjo), 'Dust My Broom' has four beats in a bar, is built on three chords and has a three-line verse in which the second line is a repeat of the first.

Robert Johnson lived a short but turbulent life as a wandering musician and enjoyed little commercial success. Although he only recorded 30 songs, most of these went on to become classics and have had a great influence on many rock musicians today. Hundreds of versions of 'Dust My Broom' have been recorded, notably by Eric Clapton, Led Zeppelin, Bob Dylan, Canned Heat and Fleetwood Mac. Johnson died when he was 26 from drinking poisoned whisky.

PERFORMANCE · HINTS & TIPS ·

This song has three different dynamic markings:

- **_p_** (_piano_ = quiet)
- **_mf_** (_mezzo forte_ = moderately loud)
- **_f_** (_forte_ = loud)

Be ready for those sections where the dynamics suddenly change. But look out also for the ⟋ at the bottom of the second page. This is a _crescendo_, which means play gradually louder.

The piano has a four-bar solo starting at bar 19 – your moment of glory. Play loudly – like a soloist – in this section.

There are several accents (>) on the second page of this song. Bar 14 and bar 26 both have repeated accented notes. Make sure that you give these notes extra emphasis. There is also an accent on the last chord of the song – make this chord louder than the notes which come before it. Be aware that the chord is placed off the beat.

This song is also in the vocals, guitar, bass and drums books so you can get together and play it in a band.

'I _believe_ I'll go back _home_'

SESSION SKILLS PLAYBACK

For your exam, you can choose either Playback or Improvising (see page 28).
If you choose Playback, you will be asked to play some music you have not seen or heard before.

In the exam, you will be given the song chart and the examiner will play a recording of the music on a CD. You will hear several two-bar phrases on the CD: you should play each of them straight back in turn. There's a rhythm track going throughout, which helps you keep in time. There should not be any gaps in the music.

In the exam you will have two chances to play with the CD:
- First time – for practice
- Second time – for assessment.

You should listen to the audio, copying what you hear; you can also read the music from the song chart. Here are some practice song charts – which are also on the CD in this book.

'I really *like* the *way* music *looks* on *paper.* It *looks* like *art* to *me*'

Steve Vai

www.trinityrock.com

Practice playback 1

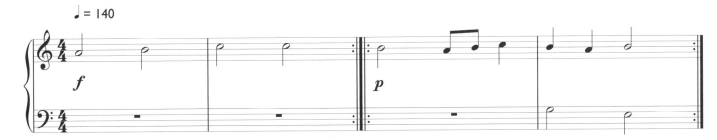

Practice playback 2

IMPROVISING

For your exam, you can choose either Playback (see page 26), or Improvising.
If you choose to improvise, you will be asked to improvise over a backing track that you haven't heard before in a specified style.

In the exam, you will be given a song chart and the examiner will play a recording of the backing track on CD. The backing track consists of a passage of music played on a loop. You should improvise a lead melodic line or rhythmic chords over it.

In the exam you will have two chances to play with the CD:
* First time – for practice
* Second time – for assessment.

Here are some practice improvisation charts which are also on the CD in this book.

Practice improvisation 1

♩ = 120 **Pop**

| Am | C | Em | Em |

Practice improvisation 2

♩ = 77 **Ballad**

| C | G | Am | G |

CHOOSING A SONG FOR YOUR EXAM

There are lots of options to help you choose your three songs for the exam.
For Songs 1 and 2, you can choose a song which is:

- from this book
- from www.trinityrock.com/downloads

Or for Song 2 you can choose a song which is:

- sheet music from a printed or online source.
- your own arrangement of a song or a song you have written yourself (see page 30).

You can play the song unaccompanied or with a backing track (minus the solo instrument). If you like, you can create a backing track yourself (or with friends), or you could add your own vocals – or both.

For Grade 1, the song should last between one and three-and-a-half minutes, and the level of difficulty should be similar to your other songs.
When choosing a song, think about:

- Does it work on my instrument?
- Are there any technical elements that are too difficult for me? (If so, perhaps save it for when you do the next grade.)
- Do I enjoy playing it?
- Does it work with my other songs to create a good set-list?

SHEET MUSIC

You must always bring an original copy of the book or a download sheet with email certificate for each song you perform in the exam. If you choose to write your own song you must provide the examiner with a copy of the sheet music.
Your music can be:

- a lead sheet with lyrics, chords and melody line
- a chord chart with lyrics
- a full score using conventional staff notation
- see page 30 for details on presenting a song you have written yourself

The title of the song and your name should be on the sheet music.

WRITING YOUR OWN SONG

You can play a song that you have written yourself for one of the choices in your exam. For Grade 1, your song should last between one and three-and-a-half minutes, so it is likely to be quite straightforward. It is sometimes difficult to know where to begin, however. Here are some suggestions for starting points:

- **A melody**: many songs are made up around a 'hook' (a short catchy melodic idea, usually only a few notes long).
Try writing a couple of ideas for hooks here:

- **A chord sequence**: a short chord sequence can provide an entire verse or chorus. Write your ideas for a chord sequence here:

- **A rhythm**: a short repeated rhythm will often underpin an entire song.
Think of a couple of short rhythms you could use here:

There are plenty of other ways of starting: perhaps with a riff or a lyric, for example.

You will also need to consider the **structure** of your song (verse and chorus, 12-bar blues, and so on), the **style** it is in (blues, hard rock, etc.), and what **instruments** it is for (solo keyboards or voice/keyboards/drums . . .).

There are many choices to be made – which is why writing a song is such a rewarding thing to do.

WRITING YOUR SONG DOWN

Rock and pop music is often written as a **lead sheet** with the lyrics (if there are any), chords and a melody line.

- As a keyboards player, you may want to write your complete part on **two staves**, as has been used for the songs in this book.

- You can, if you prefer, use a **graph** or **table** to represent your music, as long as it is clear to anyone else (including the examiner) how the song goes.

PLAYING IN A BAND

Playing in a band is exciting: it can be a lot of fun and, as with everything, the more you do it, the easier it gets. It is very different from playing on your own. Everyone contributes to the overall sound: the most important skill you need to develop is listening.

For a band to sound good, the players need to be 'together' – that mainly means keeping in time with each other, but also playing at the same volume, and with the same kind of feeling.

Your relationship with the other band members is also important. Talk with them about the music you play, the music you like, and what you'd like the band to achieve short-term and long-term.

Band rehearsals are important – you should not be late, tired or distracted by your mobile phone! Being positive makes a huge difference. Try to create a friendly atmosphere in rehearsals so that everybody feels comfortable trying out new things. Don't worry about making mistakes: that is what rehearsals are for.

'Freight Train' on page 10 and 'Dust My Broom' on page 17 are arranged for a band. You will find parts for vocals, guitar, bass and drums in the other Trinity Rock & Pop Grade 1 books. Trinity offers exams for groups of musicians at various levels. The songs arranged for bands are ideal to include as part of a set-list for these exams. Have a look at the website for more details.

HINTS AND TIPS

- Plan your band practices in advance. Think about what you would like to do before you get there.

- Record your practice sessions and listen back for sections that worked well and bits that had problems.

- In some songs you will play a supporting role; at other times you may take more of a lead. In both cases you need to listen to the overall group as well as to your own part. Be aware of how you affect the overall sound.

PLAYING WITH BACKING TRACKS

The CD contains demos and backing tracks of all the songs in the book.
The additional songs at www.trinityrock.com/downloads also come with demos and backing tracks.

- In your exam, you should play with the backing track, or you can create your own (see below).
- Keyboard players should not use auto-accompaniment features for these exams as the aim is to play with a backing track.
- The backing tracks start with a click track, which sets the tempo and helps you start accurately.
- Be careful to set the balance between the volume of the backing track and your instrument.
- Listen carefully to the backing track to ensure you are playing in time.

If you are creating your own backing track here are some further tips:
- Make sure the sound quality is of a good standard.
- Think carefully about the instruments/sounds you are putting on the backing track.
- Avoid copying what you are playing on the backing track – it should support not duplicate.
- Do you need to include a click track at the beginning?

COPYRIGHT IN A SONG

If you are a singer or songwriter it is important to know about copyright. When someone writes a song or creates an arrangement they own the copyright (sometimes called 'the rights') to that version. The copyright means that other people cannot copy it, sell it, perform it in a concert, make it available online or record it without the owner's permission or the appropriate licence. When you write a song you automatically own the copyright to it, which means that other people cannot copy your work. But, just as importantly, you cannot copy other people's work, or perform it in public without their permission or the appropriate licence.

Points to remember
- You can create a cover version of a song and play in it in an exam or other non-public performance.
- You cannot record your cover version and make your recording available to others (by copying it or uploading it to a website) without the appropriate licence.
- You do own the copyright of your own original song, which means that no one is allowed to copy it.
- You cannot copy someone else's song without their permission or the appropriate licence.